Last Flight *from* Manila

Last Flight *from* Manila

Austin Mardon | Gina Schopfer | Alexandra Gross
Taylor Croft | Jessica Jutras

A Golden Meteorite Press Book.
Printed in Canada.

First Printing: 2020

Cover Design and Typesetting by Nicole Schimpf

Telephone: 587-783-0059
Email: aamardon@yahoo.ca
Website: goldenmeteoritepress.com

Additional copies can be ordered from:
Suite 103 11919-82 Street NW
Edmonton, AB
T5B 2W4
CANADA

ISBN: (paperback)

Table of Contents

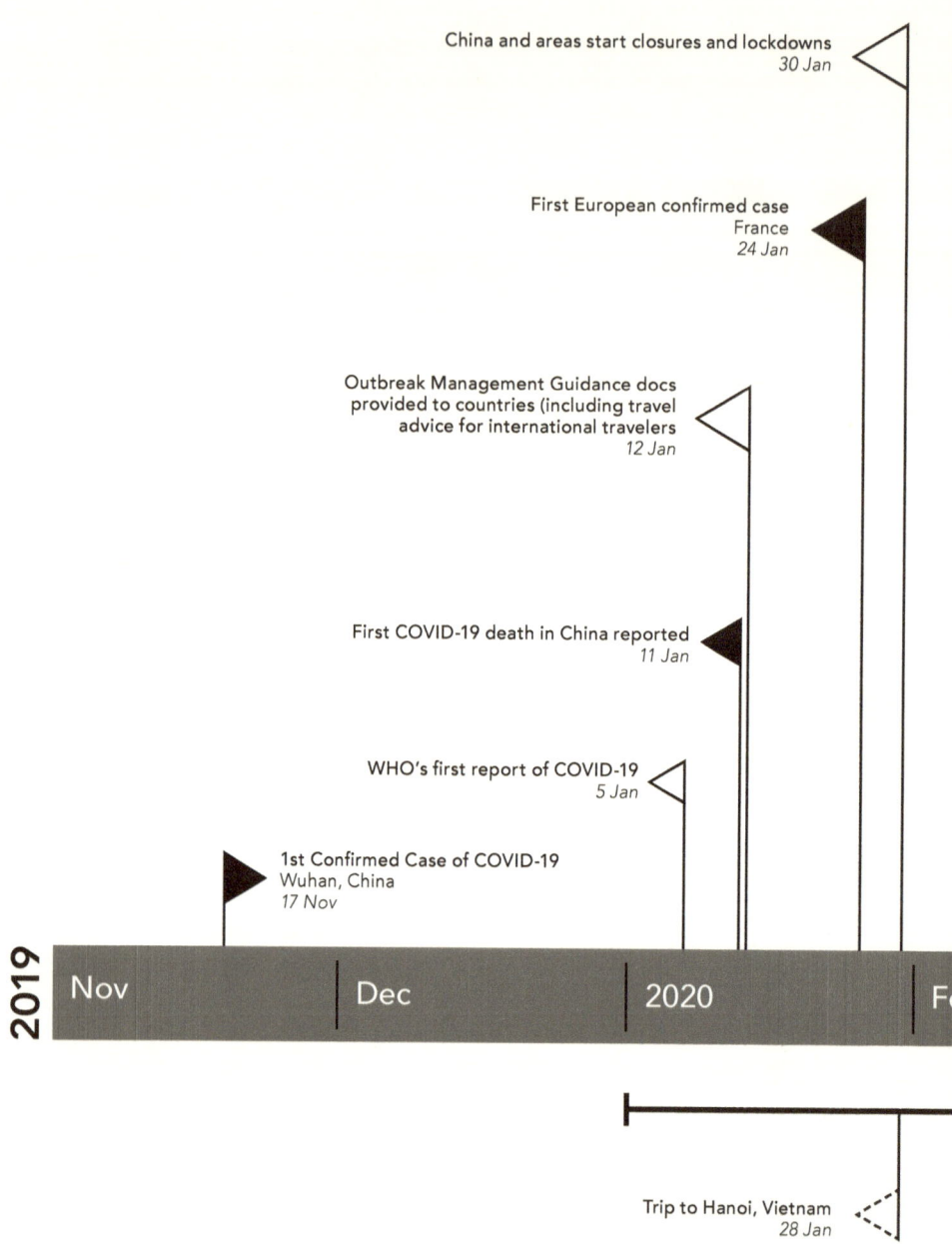

China and areas start closures and lockdowns
30 Jan

First European confirmed case
France
24 Jan

Outbreak Management Guidance docs
provided to countries (including travel
advice for international travelers
12 Jan

First COVID-19 death in China reported
11 Jan

WHO's first report of COVID-19
5 Jan

1st Confirmed Case of COVID-19
Wuhan, China
17 Nov

2019

Nov

Dec

2020

Fe

Trip to Hanoi, Vietnam
28 Jan

Last Flight from Manila
Timeline

COVID-19 Timeline

First COVID-19 death in France
5 Feb

Tablighi Jamaat at Jamek Mosque in
Sri Petaling, Kuala Lumpur - the largest
spike in cases in the area
27 Feb

Trudeau and the Government of Canada
call all travelers home
15 Mar

Philippines enters mandatory quarentine/lockdown
16 Mar

Malaysia enters lockdown
18 Mar

Mar   Apr   May   **2020**

Two moths ahead, Canada is still
in quarantine/self-isolation
19 May

Arrive home and begin two week
self-isolation period
15 Mar

Many travelers are returning home
13 Mar

x

Foreword

IN MARCH OF 2020, the world came to a standstill. Businesses closed, schools transitioned to online learning, and all but essential employees either lost their jobs or were required to work from home. Social contact was limited to those within a single household, festivals and sports were cancelled, and short term plans for the future were erased. This global standstill was the result of a worldwide pandemic unlike any the world had seen in its history.

In late 2019, a new coronavirus disease called COVID-19 emerged in Wuhan, China. On December 31st, authorities from China contacted the World Health Organization (WHO) about several cases of an unknown illness producing symptoms similar to pneumonia in patients in the city of Wuhan[1]. The virus spread globally over the early months of 2020. During the month of January, cases appeared in 23 different countries across Asia, Europe, North America and Australia. On January 30th, the WHO publicly declared the outbreak a Public Health Emergency of International Concern (PHEIC). In the month of February, 37 more countries reported their first cases. By February 9th, the number of coronavirus deaths had surpassed the total number of deaths during the SARS-CoV(Severe Acute Respiratory Syndrome) epidemic, the latter of which had an outbreak that lasted about six months. Despite developing and spreading at an unprecedented rate, it wasn't until March 11th that the WHO finally declared the COVID-19 outbreak a pandemic.

In the following weeks, many nations began to take action. The border between Canada and the United States was closed to all but essential travel, and one-third of the entire world's population went into lockdown in the month of March alone. Preventative measures were also

---

1   To read the complete timeline of events, see Kantis et al., 2020.

put in place very rapidly during this month, and most individuals living and travelling abroad were advised to return home as soon as possible. Though top governmental officials across the world attempted to predict a timeline for the outbreak, doing so proved difficult. The virulence of the pandemic stretched months longer than initially predicted, bringing a significant loss of work and social life for most individuals, as well as economic hardship at a level unseen since the Great Depression of the 1930s.

On March 14, 2020, Canadian Prime Minister, Justin Trudeau, urged Canadians abroad to return home while they still could, as the growing number of COVID-19 cases in Canada had prompted national and international travel restrictions. "Airlines have cancelled flights. New restrictions may be imposed with little warning. Your travel plans may be severely disrupted, and you may be forced to remain outside of Canada longer than expected," the ministry said in an email to registered Canadians abroad[2]. This message was enough to alert the majority of Canadian travellers, and most returned home before April.

However, the decision to return to Canada was difficult for many Canadians travelling or living abroad. Whether at home or abroad, COVID-19 posed a substantial health threat and disruption to day-to-day life. They could expect to face the same challenges as the everyday Canadian citizen during the crisis, along with unique challenges faced by travellers. Many were left without a source of income; those who did not become unemployed due to COVID-19 did not qualify for Canada's Emergency Response Benefit, and finding new employment under these dire economic circumstances proved nearly impossible. Finding a place to live or stay also proved challenging without a regular income source, as did the inability to predict how long these restrictions and economic downturn would last.

By the beginning of June, less than six months after the virus was first reported in China, the total number of confirmed cases globally had approached seven million. 188 countries had reported cases and the total number of COVID-19 related deaths nearly hit the 400,000 mark. In Canada alone, approximately 7,800 deaths had been reported. Nei-

---

2   To read the complete timeline of events, see Kantis et al., 2020.

ther effective treatments nor a vaccine was yet available, making social distancing, handwashing, and the wearing of masks the most effective measures in preventing the spread of the virus. As social contact with others continued to be discouraged, many remained stuck in the same circumstances they had been in since March.

With many unknown factors still to be uncovered, the COVID-19 has caused much fear and uncertainty. Some individuals show severe symptoms to the infection while others do not show any at all, making its spread difficult to track[3]. It is not known how long the virus survives on surfaces or how the virus can be treated. The leading treatment at present is the use of ventilators to help individuals with severe symptoms breathe[4]. As predicted by the WHO in 2018 in a document on managing epidemics, "anxiety or even panic and confusion" about the COVID-19 pandemic are distinctly felt by the general public to this day.

In the following chapters, we tell the inspired story of Colbie and her best friend Emma, two Canadians in their early twenties who returned home to Edmonton, Alberta, Canada from Southeast Asia on March 17th. Their experience is illustrative of the profound uncertainty that many felt, whether at home or abroad, at the height of the pandemic. At the time of writing, we do not know how or when this worldwide conflict will be resolved. Of one thing we can be certain: it will be a presence in our lives for a considerable length of time - possibly many years. The magnitude of this event has left the world we once knew irrevocably altered. Even as restrictions become slightly more lenient, long-distance travel remains close to non-existent, and most individuals remain close to home and mindfully secluded to flatten the curve and protect those most vulnerable to the virus. We can expect travel - a highlight of many of our lives, integral to the human experience - to be changed forever.

---

3   The Globe and Mail, 2020.
4   Government of Canada, 2020a.

Chapter 1

THERE IS NO EXPERIENCE comparable to air travel. I've always considered airports magical places filled with reunited loved ones and jet-setters taking off on adventures. The miracle of flight alone is still worth marvelling at, despite all the technological advances that have occurred since the first flight of the Wright brothers in 1903. When I was growing up, my family frequently travelled, which is why trips are my favourite aspect of planning my future. I love diving into the unfamiliar and gaining an understanding of how others live. There is so much value in grasping firsthand the differences between cultures. Even though it is easier than ever for human beings to connect with barely any time and space barriers, it is eye-opening to see the spectacular diversity of life that still exists in our world. I never imagined we would all have to face a common challenge together, regardless of geographical location, especially since we all live so differently. Yet that view was permanently altered for me in the year of 2020.

In January of 2020, my best friend Emma and I set off to visit and work for my Great Aunt Susan in George Town: the capital city of the island of Penang in Malaysia. Though born in Canada, she has lived there for the past twelve years. She runs a teaching English as a second language program called 'myTESOL Penang.' Three years ago, I lived with her and took her English teaching program, followed by a practicum at a local orphanage. I adored Malaysia, and now that I had finished my degree, I had saved up to reward myself with a post-graduation trip. Emma had been to the United Kingdom once for a family reunion but hadn't travelled outside of the country beyond that, with the exception of a few trips down to The United States. Still, I knew she would be an easygoing travel companion. Her positivity and curiosity added to every adventure, and she was so excited to venture further than she had gone before.

I sat in a small window seat at the very back of the plane as Emma flipped through her Malaysian travel guide for what I thought was likely to be the fiftieth time. I tilted my head to the left to rest on my neck pillow, and the cool window next to me as my eyes blinked to stay open. "It's probably better if I just stay up," I thought to myself. "That'll help me adjust to the time change." As anyone who has taken a long-haul flight before knows, this is easier said than done.

We landed in Kuala Lumpur - the capital of Malaysia - at about three in the morning on January 10th, also known as one in the afternoon on the 9th back home. I remembered the time difference being such an adjustment the last time I was here. When it's morning in Malaysia, it's evening at home, and vice versa. Though it created a greater disconnect from everything I found comfort in, it helped me stay off my phone awaiting messages from my friends and family. I was able to live in the moment more.

Disoriented, we made our way through the Kuala Lumpur airport to reach a conveyor belt of taxi stands. The salespeople were yelling from every direction to encourage us to come towards theirs. We were helped by a lovely middle-aged woman who directed us towards a taxi sitting right outside. It was pitch-black out, and without a view, the drive dragged on. I was already eagerly anticipating the following morning. The long taxi-ride finally came to an end. After checking in to our 24-hour hostel and taking a quick shower to rinse off the last 23 hours and three flights, we were out.

I awoke suddenly at six in the morning, feeling exhausted, but like I had slept in. It made sense - at home, it was about four in the afternoon. Feeling a desperate need to stretch my legs, I walked down the stairs to the hostel entrance and stumbled out the door to feel the hot and humid air hit my face. I decided to take a stroll around the block - I was awake, and nothing could be done about it. Walking down the street, I passed many men and women already setting up their stalls and preparing food to sell. The smells that still seemed foreign to me brought back memories from my first time in Malaysia, and I felt comfort where I hadn't expected. Stopping for a moment to revel in the sounds and smells, I took a seat on a weathered bench. I opened my phone to check the news.

China reports its first death to novel coronavirus.

The 61-year-old man had been a regular customer at a market in Wuhan and had died from symptoms caused by the virus. The story had left me feeling disheartened and I wondered just how severe the impacts of this disease were likely to be, especially with Chinese New Year just around the corner. I was excited for the New Year celebrations, having experienced it in Malaysia a couple of years earlier. Its hype was well-deserved, as Chinese New Year is an even bigger celebration than Christmas or any other major holiday here. During Chinese New Year, hundreds of millions of people travel across China, Malaysia, and other Asian countries to celebrate with family. "I hope this doesn't prevent any festivities," I thought to myself as I put my phone back in my pocket, stood up and continued walking, leaving thoughts of the virus back on the bench.

Kuala Lumpur is the ultimate city of contrast. Luxurious high-rise condos boasting infinity pools sit next to small ramshackle shops and homes. Women in headscarves and burkas walk alongside women in tank tops and short shorts. As I walk down the street, I pass a mosque, church, and Buddhist temple within the same two blocks. Malaysia's variety flows together peacefully and harmoniously. It makes both cities and rural areas wondrous for travellers by offering the chance to experience so many different cultures and try so many kinds of food. I think that's the main reason it has always been one of my favourite countries to visit.

We spent the next two days wandering around the city, sampling street food at the night market, and venturing out to the Batu Caves. The Batu Caves is a vast limestone hill consisting of a series of caves and temples. It is one of the most revered Hindu shrines existing outside of India, and its size is nothing less than astounding. The heat was a difficult adjustment, especially after coming from the depths of a -35°C Alberta winter - with daily temperatures usually sitting around mid 30°C. From the Batu Caves, we caught a four-hour bus ride to George Town, where upon arrival, we haggled with a local taxi for a cheap ride to Aunt Susan's condo.

Emma was so excited to be here. She had been a dear friend to me since we met during my first month of university. Even being new friends, we seemed to understand each other in a way that solidified our friendship for the next five years. As it was her first time in Asia, she was trying to soak everything in and visibly appreciated every moment. I immediately loved having her as a travel companion. As a more seasoned traveller, I sometimes forget to take a step back and enjoy what's right in front of me. Emma reminded me to do that.

"That Indian restaurant last night was the best I've ever had, I swear!" Emma was a bit of a foodie and had already taken about fifty pictures of our dinners, fruit breakfasts, and sweet corn desserts. "Your aunt wanted to take us out for food tonight, right? I wonder where she'll take us..." she trailed off as she became fully immersed by the colourful images of murgh makhani, chicken tikka masala, and mango lassi on her phone.

As we passed jungle forests and lush, green cliffs nearly as tall as the mountains at home, I became overcome with the excitement of returning to one of my favourite places in the world. Suddenly, the thirteen-kilometre dual carriageway toll bridge that connects George Town and the island of Penang to the mainland rose into view - we were finally about to arrive.

Chapter

OUR CAB STOPPED at the gated entrance of Aunt Susan's beach condo, where a security guard in standard Malaysian uniform stood. His bright red hat popped flamboyantly against the white backdrop of the condo and large metal gate. We tried to explain that our aunt lived here, but didn't make much progress because of the language barrier. It was an instant reminder of being in Malaysia three years ago. Luckily, Aunt Susan appeared as she stepped out of the condominium's glass door and began enthusiastically waving at us with a beaming smile on her face. I always loved seeing her. She was one of those people who could instantly put you in a good mood with her kindness and contagious smile.

After Aunt Susan spoke a few short words in Malay to the guard, he pressed the button, opening the gate. He apologized profusely, smiled and waved after us as we stepped into the gated community. She gave us each a massive hug as we passed the threshold. In Canada, this would be a much more expensive living situation. The condo looked lovely, with modern features, a large outdoor pool next to indoor fitness amenities, and a path that stepped out directly onto the beach overlooking the ocean. This part of the ocean is called the Strait of Malacca and has been the primary shipping channel between the Indian and Pacific oceans since the 1600s.

"So, how was the trip? Many stops? That journey always nearly kills me. You can see why I don't do it often! I have everything I need right here," she boasted, pointing with both hands as we gazed off the balcony and across the glassy water.

"It wasn't as bad as we expected!" I promised. "We were so excited to arrive that it didn't phase us."

"Wonderful! That's the spirit! I have the perfect welcome meal planned if you ladies don't mind a short walk. It's about two minutes down the road."

Aunt Susan has always reminded me of my grandma. She loves to chat, and her words fill most of the conversation. She's very quirky and seems to pick up interests and really run with them. She gave us a tour of her modern, two-bedroom condo with a breathtaking ocean view, and showed us her plethora of exotic plants. At the same time, we caught her up on all the family ongoings. It seemed she didn't regularly chat with anyone from home, besides the occasional message with her two children living back in Canada. After less than an hour of getting acquainted, we headed out to try one of her favourite Korean restaurants down the road. The service and food were incredible. Though there was a language barrier once again, there was an apparent effort put into making us feel welcome and making sure we were enjoying ourselves. The smiling faces were so uplifting. Emma offered to pay for our meal as a thank-you for allowing her to come on the trip. At eighty Malaysian ringgit - only about twenty-five Canadian dollars - the bill amazed her. We took the short walk back to the condo slowly while enjoying the warm breeze drifting past from the beach alongside us.

George Town sits on the island of Penang and is known as one of the food capitals of Southeast Asia. This is a huge part of why I wanted to return. Of course, I love the atmosphere, the warm weather, and the beach; but the food is a massive draw, and the variety is what makes it so outstanding. Though western options are limited in comparison to other types of food, this was the perfect arrangement for us. After being away for months, the occasional burger and fries can be inviting, but it's never at the top of my list when I'm here. I noticed a few small and dimly lit Thai, Malay, and Israeli restaurants that I had tried in the past, and made a mental note to return.

Our feet dragged as we shuffled through the small entryway door into the condo. We said a brief goodnight to Aunt Susan before heading to the guest room. It was set up beautifully with decorative towels, a mountain of local snacks, toilet paper - as most public bathrooms didn't offer any, and insect repellent lotion. I couldn't even hold myself awake long enough to look through it all, so I changed and immediately flopped into bed.

I woke up suddenly, covered in sweat, momentarily forgetting where I was. My hand reached across the bed to find my phone. Although the clock read only 5:11 a.m., I felt wide awake. I was still adjusting to the time change. Luckily, this gave me some time to get settled and clean myself up before starting the day. Aunt Susan said it was customary to shower whenever one returned home, or at least to wash hands and feet. This was because of the heat and dirtiness outside that made the spread of bacteria all the more likely. After a refreshing shower, I unpacked my clothes from my suitcase, hung them up to avoid mustiness, and then laid back in bed to read my travel book. The sunrise through the bedroom's sliding glass door felt inviting and allowed me to settle into a peaceful morning, which I needed badly after the past couple of days.

Nearly two hours later, I heard bustling outside the bedroom door. Wandering outside, I looked across the living room to see Aunt Susan on the other side of the island rummaging through the kitchen.

"Oh, you are up! I figured it'd be another early morning for you. No Emma yet?"

I shook my head. "Still sleepin' soundly."

I spent the morning answering Aunt Susan's questions about my university experience, dating lives, friends, and plans for the future. She offered advice based on her experiences, which I always loved to hear about.

"You know, I'd say I have about a decade left of this, then I'll need someone to take over for me! If you like it here enough to come back again after this, there will always be a spot for you. We loved having you at the school." I was delighted at the idea.

After Emma emerged, we made ourselves a simple breakfast of peanut butter and banana toast with greek yogurt. The three of us headed out for school at 7:30 a.m. We took Aunt Susan's car down the road about ten minutes before reaching the school. I loved this drive because it went along the coast. I used to take this bus route every morning and stare out at the shades of turquoise and electric blue glimmering past me. The school itself was in a three-story shopping complex on the third floor. In the humid Malaysian heat, three flights of stairs are more than enough.

A tall, pale woman greeted us. She was about Aunt Susan's age, wearing a floor-length flowery skirt, beige blouse, and soft pink hijab. I recognized her immediately. "Suraya!" I exclaimed while striding over to meet her grand embrace.

"I hear you're going to be back with us for awhile, Colbie! We couldn't be more thrilled." She exclaimed, smiling.

"Thank you! I've been wanting to come back since I left."

"That was three years ago already, yes? My goodness, it feels like no time at all. And did you bring someone with you this time?" She smiled even wide, eyeing up my friend.

Emma smiled back and reached out her hand to introduce herself. I could tell she was a little nervous. Though she became TESOL certified online, this would be her first time actually teaching students. It can be nerve-wracking, and it takes time to learn how to communicate as a teacher. Confidence is a massive part of it. I knew she would be great, but I understood her mild nervosity.

Chapter 3

WHILE SURAYA GAVE us a tour of the facility, I noticed hardly anything had changed since I had been there last. It was a small building, but they made the most of the space. As you walked in, you could find two small classrooms along the left side of the wall, and on the right - a small reception desk with a cute bell. Around the corner, you would find yourself in a breakroom of sorts, with a couple of small tables, a coffee station, a sink, refrigerator, microwave, and doors to the washrooms.

Past this, there were two small classrooms. One of which was occupied by couches for "tea time" - a half-hour slot given to students in the middle of each school day for discussion. This allowed everyone to get to know each other and practice their English.

On one of the couches sat a tall, young man with sleek dark hair and a furrowed brow. He was looking down at a notebook in his hands. As soon as he noticed others in the room, however, his face shifted to a smile.

"You must be Colbie and Emma! I'm Josh. I heard you would be arriving today." He extended his hand to greet us with a firm handshake. Josh had grown up in the city of London in the U.K. He had been teaching at the school for nearly six months. "I'll be out of here soon, though. It sounds like you'll be taking on my role and that of another teacher finishing up her term." We would have the next two weeks together before he moved on to do some sightseeing in the Philippines. His plans to swim with whale sharks in Cebu, visit the beautiful hidden beaches and lagoons of Palawan, and take in Manila's bright lights sounded incredible. The Philippines was another country on my list of places I hoped to see.

We had to keep the introductions brief, as there was work to be done. Although today would be a light day for Emma and I, everyone else was in full swing. Even more so, since we were now sitting in on lessons. I considered myself quite familiar with leading a class in an English lesson. I reminded myself of the vital TESOL strategies I had learned previously, as I watched the other teachers. It is essential to build a firm foundation for the lesson by focusing on a tiny piece of information. If you use a few vocabulary words or a grammar rule and don't move on until that piece is understood, you can build from there. Knowing this made my day easy as pie, while Emma's felt a little more demanding. She furiously scribbled down every word she could as she watched a lesson that taught the days of the month.

At tea time, Suraya and I continued our conversation from earlier as Josh and Emma walked over. After a brief pause in the conversation, Josh took the lead by asking a question we'd be hearing for months to come. "Anyone know what's happening with this coronavirus? I can't believe how fast it's spreading. I heard there are already cases in Malaysia."

"I don't believe there are yet. Thailand has had its first confirmed case, and that's also the first reported case located outside of China. It will come, though. It's clearly already made its way through airports. It's just a matter of time," I responded, "but I'm sure it'll be handled before things escalate much worse than that."

"Well, that's the thing. There's no way to know right now," replied Suraya.

She continues, "I saw that the World Health Organization released an outbreak management guide containing all the information they've been able to obtain so far. Based on what they've learned from the SARS and MERS outbreaks, infection and prevention control guidance for respiratory transmission is pretty much all the advice they can give so far. Washing your hands is the big point, of course. Susan's always been aware of her student demographics; most cultural norms place a high emphasis on cleanliness and preventing the spread of germs. Japanese culture, for example, is often very attentive to that sort of thing. Nearly half of our student population is from Japan, and Susan will want to ensure all her students feel comfortable."

As Suraya finished her thought, Susan rang the bell for classes to resume. I wanted to know more and was eager to continue the conversation. How threatening was the virus? What were the chances of it getting to us, and what would come of my time away if that possibility became more likely? Emma and I had lots of travelling around Southeast Asia planned.

As the week went on, we continued to sit in on classes and met some of the other teachers and students. Margaret and Louisa were sisters from Sweden and taught English at the school. They were about our age and were very close with each other. Of the two sisters, Louisa often took the lead in conversations and was a little more outspoken. The pair came as a set, and we enjoyed spending time with both of them. We met many students who adored us and made us feel so welcome.

One student stood out to me the most. Wendy, a 19-year-old student learning English at myTESOL, was attached to my hip most of the week. She had an extensive list of questions about my life, and I didn't mind answering personal ones with her. She was as curious about others as I was, which resulted in a special friendship. We both felt we could share openly with one another. During tea time on Friday of our first week, Wendy asked me if I'd be teaching her class. When I told her that I wouldn't be, but my friend Emma would, she turned towards Emma and smiled, trying to be supportive but still looking slightly disappointed. It gave everyone an innocent giggle. Luckily, Emma seemed to have more fans than I did. The students were kind, curious, and eager to make friends. It was a refreshing attitude to interact with, and was an aspect of teaching that's easy to love.

We started teaching our classes after two weeks of sitting in on lessons. I ran the standard course I had learned the first time here and had been observing for the last couple of weeks. Every day we started with introductions. We knew each other's names after the early days. Still, it gave students practice introducing themselves and a way to learn conversation starters. For the rest of the morning, we'd tackle a vocabulary lesson. During the second part of the day, we would apply the morning's vocab lesson with a grammar lesson. My students were mainly young adults, except for one young girl from northern Malaysia who was twelve, and her two parents. I always loved teaching people outside of grade school because they tend to value education more than the average student.

I felt comfortable in Penang almost instantly. I quickly became attached to the students and couldn't imagine how things could get any better. The coronavirus topic came up nearly daily that week, but we weren't thinking too deeply about it. Though we knew it was becoming a real problem, it still seemed to be far away and might not even impact us at all. I never saw the point in worrying about something that couldn't be changed, so it remained out of my mind for the most part.

Chapter 4

"TODAY ONE OF MY STUDENTS asked me why we say 'on' the first when talking about a certain date, but we say 'in' June. I got so flustered. I tried to say that there are many days in a month, so if we're talking about something that broad, we say 'in,' and one date is more specific."

I burst out laughing. "Did she understand your explanation?" Emma looked down and shook her head as I waved myself with a makeshift fan I had made from a brochure in class. We were waiting for the bus after a slow day. We were halfway through our second week of teaching already, and time had flown by because we were filling our days and were out like a light by the early evening. The heat exhausted us and was taking more time to adjust to than the time difference did. Emma's mention of dates roused thoughts of the coming ones and I fell into day dreams of expeditions.

With Chinese New Year just around the corner, we were overflowing with excitement! The local people get incredibly excited for the New Year in Penang, and the streets become unbelievably crowded. In some ways, the celebration reminds me of Christmas in Canada; families get together to enjoy each other's company, and people look forward to it for weeks. Food is abundant and monetary gifts are popular. The way that people go out and celebrate collectively in the streets during the Chinese New Year is enrapturing. We overheard many people exchanging "Gong

Xi Fa Cai." A phrase people say during the holiday to wish others good luck, wealth and prosperity for the New Year. The coming year was the year of the rat - it's the first in the Chinese zodiac cycle and occurs every 12 years.

I remember experiencing the New Year in Penang a few years ago – it was the year of the rooster. There were lion dances and fireworks, and I celebrated into the night. On the actual day of Chinese New Year, a lovely Korean family invited me to their home. Jenny, an English student of mine at the time, was the mother and wife of this family. When I first arrived, she told me they had prepared a fantastic meal, with plenty of Korean and Japanese dishes, drinks, and her famous chocolate cake for dessert. Everyone spoke in English, which I knew was for my benefit. Their hospitality was surreal; I had never experienced a family so accepting. Jenny wiped food from my face while I was eating, held my hand, and hugged me throughout the evening - touching everything with a loving warmth.

We were also excited about the holiday because Aunt Susan was going to give us some time off to do some travelling. At this time of year, many students were away from school, so a full staff wasn't necessary. She had asked us a couple of days ago if we wanted to take the following 5-day week off. We agreed instantaneously.

Deciding where to go next is always tricky since it means choosing not to go somewhere else. We had a surplus of places to visit in the future, especially being in Penang. A three-hour ferry ride could take us to the Langkawi Islands, said to be the "Jewel of Kedah" with its turquoise sea and pristine beaches. A two-hour drive could take us into Thailand. I've been to Bangkok before, but if we went further north to Chiang Mai, we would feast on some of the best street food in the world.

At the top of our destination list, though, was Northern Vietnam. We had heard phenomenal things about Hanoi - the capital city, Ha Long Bay - with its magnificent emerald waters, and Hoi An - a beautifully preserved Ancient Town. The inexpensive cost of the whole trip, including travel there and back to George Town, was a bonus.

Later that afternoon, after stopping at home to rest for a while, we met Wendy at a small shopping complex near myTESOL. Emma needed a new pair of shoes, and she had kindly offered to show us a few spots she liked to shop. We grabbed food at the food court from a buffet-style restaurant. I tried a fish head for the first time and was surprised to find out it wasn't terrible! Admittedly, it isn't my first choice. Wendy asked us about our plans for Vietnam and passed on a few travel tips she had heard from her friends. She didn't have the chance to travel often herself, beyond going to and from China with her parents, where she lived for a portion of the year. Wendy had explained that her father went back and forth between Penang and Shanghai for work. Her family had a beautiful second home in Straits Quay - a wealthy coastal neighbourhood not far from Aunt Susan's. It had a massive shopping centre on the harbour that showcased high-end restaurants with guests that loved to sit on the patios along the boardwalk. Wendy admitted she didn't make it there often since her studies held her focus and planned to attend University in China in the fall.

During our conversation, I asked Wendy how the coronavirus was developing in China and if she knew anyone affected. She told us that her family lives much further north from Wuhan. The virus hadn't impacted her family yet, but she acknowledged things were becoming more serious. We moved on to a new topic quickly. Despite being curious, the only new information we had was that the virus greatly affected respiratory systems and was now spreading across the map to places like Europe. Wendy moved along by inviting us to her family's home for an evening celebration of the Chinese New Year before we left for Vietnam. We cheerfully accepted the invitation.

Two days later, Emma and I strolled over to Wendy's home in Straits Quay to kick-off their weeks of celebrations. We spent the evening drinking, playing games, and observing Wendy's family take part in their New Year customs. Wendy's grandparents even offered Emma and I little red envelopes with some money. We tried to decline, but they wouldn't have it - we were guests in their house, and it was tradition to pass on wealth to one another. Although we felt awkward at first, we appreciated being included in the festivities. The amount of food was astounding, and my excitement grew as I breathed in the aromas wafting towards me.

Later on, we watched the fireworks from her balcony. There would be fireworks nearly every night for the next couple of weeks. This precursor to Chinese New Year, paired with the one I attended beforehand, became two of my favourite experiences. My gratitude exulted me from being a part of this merriment; it was the perfect send-off to start a new adventure in Vietnam tomorrow.

Chapter 5

OUR FIRST INTRODUCTION TO VIETNAM was its capital city - Hanoi, a bustling commercial and cultural hub. To say this city was busy would be an understatement. Remembering the popular video game, "Frogger," I used to play as a kid, I made parallels with how I felt trying to get around this city, dodging masses of traffic to get from one side of the narrow streets to the other. After a long day of enthusiastically exploring, admiring the mix of historical monuments, contemporary buildings, and French colonial influences, we returned to our hostel. We booked a two-day boat trip in Ha Long Bay - one of Vietnam's most naturally picturesque destinations - for the next day. Hanoi was a spectacular starting point, and we couldn't wait to explore more of what Vietnam had to offer.

After a quick breakfast at the hostel's rooftop cafe the following morning, we set out to board a small bus only a few blocks away. At the start of the six-hour ride, an exuberant, hilarious Vietnamese man welcomed everyone and introduced himself as our tour guide. He gave a theatrical history of Ha Long Bay, explaining that the name means 'descending dragon.' Legend is, shortly after becoming a country, the people of Vietnam had to fight off hostile invaders. The Jade Emperor - leader of the lands - called upon the Gods to send a Mother Dragon and her children to defeat the enemies. The Dragons did not hesitate and ferociously set the invaders ablaze. Left behind were giant protective emeralds creating a barrier impossible to penetrate, and peace in Ha Long. It is said that the family of Dragons did not return to the Heavens, but instead adopted the form of human-beings and lived among the people of the Islands.

I stepped off the bus to see the beach for the first time. I had seen plenty of beautiful pictures of Ha Long Bay online and in travel books, but to see it in person was truly astonishing. We boarded the boat, and I felt instantly at peace. I was grateful to be on this little trip away from Malaysia. I knew that without phone service, no access to any news, and no one in sight but the people on this boat, that it would be easy to forget about anything outside the beautiful vast bay and the wondrous islets of limestone that dotted its horizon.

After spending two days kayaking through caves, swimming in the crystal waters, and drifting through the bay by boat, we arrived back on land. We boarded another bus and then a train to make our way to Da Nang. This port town is one of Vietnam's largest municipalities but held such a relaxed atmosphere that we barely noticed the high population. We enjoyed a relaxed beach day soaking up the sun, laying in the soft sand, and swimming leisurely before making our way to Hoi An.

This city was the one I had been most excited to explore and was our final stop in Vietnam. As a UNESCO World Heritage Site, Hoi An is renowned for its preservation of the blended foreign and indigenous Asian infrastructure. With only a few short days to take in all the wonder Hoi An had to offer, we had a full itinerary. We dropped our bags off at our hostel and hit the ground running. The first stop was to see one of Vietnam's most iconic attractions: the Japanese covered bridge. Wandering through the incredible architecture of Hoi An's Ancient Town had us awestruck.

The following day, after an afternoon on a cruise through the Thu Bon River, we took a much-needed break from the Vietnamese heat in our fan-cooled hostel dorm. Emma bent over her top bunk to look at me in the bed below and thrust her phone towards me, displaying an opened page to a Vietnam travel blog.

"I just read that Hoi An has been dubbed the bánh mì capital of Vietnam! I must get my hands on one." She was talking about Vietnamese baguette sandwiches that were sold on nearly every street corner here

- I was surprised we hadn't already picked one up. After a little while longer in our chilled room, we ventured out to grab a quick bite and see whether this claim held true. We found a small street vendor a couple of blocks from our hostel and ordered two of the sandwiches. We both enthusiastically agreed between bites that Hoi An had to be the home of the best bánh mì.

We ate them while sitting on a small bench in a park just outside what looked like an elementary school. I couldn't help but notice the number of people walking the streets with face masks. It wasn't uncommon to see the Vietnamese locals cover their faces below the eyes during the day with fabric pieces to protect from sun exposure. Still, these masks looked more medical and weren't at all like those makeshift, fashion-oriented coverings. I knew these were a product of the growing coronavirus concern.

The peace of mind I felt on the boat back in Ha Long Bay had dissipated. I tried to keep my mind off the virus while on this short trip to Vietnam. However, not only were there a growing amount of medical masks being worn, there were also daily coronavirus news updates, which were a constant acknowledgement that this virus was becoming more than just China's issue. It was now rampantly travelling across Southeast Asian countries like Thailand, Malaysia, and just south of Vietnam's borders and seeing the precautions heightened made it all the more real. I put the thoughts out of my mind for now, though. We had one last night in Vietnam. We had planned to spend it working our way through Hoi An's eccentric night market. I didn't want thoughts of this virus to prohibit me from thoroughly enjoying the experience.

The market was an enchanting mix of soft lights, sweet and spicy fragrances from food stands, and booths full of trinkets and toys. Tourists and locals mingled. I watched bargains being made between buyers and vendors; noticed dishes on food carts that I had never seen before; felt the brush of kids chasing each other excitedly through the steady flow of people passing through the market; and admired the artisans hand making unique pieces. I was fully immersed in the culture around me. "What a perfect way to end our time in Vietnam," I thought to myself as we continued to make our way through the maze of stalls.

Chapter 6

AFTER AN EXTRAORDINARY WEEK in Vietnam, we arrived back in George Town on the evening of February 4th. While my head was still full of all of the beautiful sights, smells, flavours, and sounds of Vietnam, I was looking forward to returning to Malaysia. Penang had begun to feel like home. As the taxi pulled up to the gate of Aunt Susan's community, a feeling of security and contentment fell over me like a warm blanket. I had missed my quirky aunt and the school. Although planning lessons was a lot of work, seeing those lightbulb moments in the eyes of the students I had the privilege to teach gave me satisfaction and purpose. Nothing could compare.

When we stepped into the house, the smell of nasi lemak - a Malay dish consisting of rice cooked in coconut milk and pandan leaf, wafted towards us. My stomach audibly grumbled in response.

"Hello!" Emma called out as the door swung shut behind us.

Aunt Susan poked her head around the corner. "Hi, girls! Dinner's almost finished. Go unpack and get cleaned up, and then you can tell me all about your trip!"

After showering and changing out of our travel clothes into something clean and comfy, we returned to the dining room to find dinner being served. As we sat down, Emma launched into a story about a restaurant we had visited in Hanoi. She asked Aunt Susan whether she had ever tried bún chá, a Vietnamese dish of pork and noodles.

"This is delicious, by the way," Emma added, indicating to her plate with her fork. Aunt Susan smiled, but it didn't quite reach her eyes.

"Is everything okay here?" I asked tentatively. Aunt Susan wore her heart on her sleeve, and there was definitely something weighing down her normally exuberant enthusiasm for every conversation topic. Her smile fell and she sighed.

"Does it have to do with the virus?" Emma asked, echoing my thoughts.

"Yes. It's the school. I'm considering closing it temporarily."

My jaw nearly dropped, "Completely?" Emma and I exchanged glances.

"That's right. I've already lost ten students since the two of you left. Just this afternoon, Wendy's mother informed me that she didn't feel her daughters were safe, and they wouldn't be coming back on Monday. She's probably right. I can't help but wonder if it's irresponsible to keep the school open." The pain in her voice was audible, and I understood why. Although myTESOL Penang was a massive success in George Town now, she had spent ten years building it to that point, and it had been far from easy. Deciding to close it was unthinkable to me. The fact that she was seriously considering it drove home how serious the situation was becoming in Malaysia.

"What about the students who want to continue going to school?" I asked. "Shouldn't the school stay open for them?"

"Maybe. But maybe not. I just don't know what the right thing to do is. I won't make a decision right away, but …Oh, I'm so sorry, girls, but I can't have you back to teach. Not right now, at least. I've lost too many students already. If you come into the school after having been on all those buses and ferries, I might lose the rest."

"No, don't worry. I totally understand," I assured her. My head was spinning, though, making me feel dizzy.

"Yeah," Emma added. "When things get better, we'll come back. I'm sure it won't be long."

"Thank you for being so understanding." Aunt Susan reached across the table and squeezed both of our hands. We were quiet for a moment as we ate. "Now. Tell me more about Vietnam. Did you make it to Hoi An?" We told her the rest of our stories, but a new weight was on our shoulders, making the conversation feel strained.

That night, I couldn't sleep. Part of the adventure of moving to Malaysia had been to travel, but teaching was a significant highlight. With Aunt Susan considering shutting down the school - even temporarily, other businesses were undoubtedly doing the same. After dinner, Emma and I had reasoned that we could possibly do more travelling while we waited, and return to the school once it reopened. Now though, as I was stuck in a whirlwind of anxious thoughts, I was beginning to doubt how plausible that would be, too.

Over the next few days, things really began to change. Almost overnight, schools across most of Asia started to shut down. Aunt Susan followed suit, and Emma and I were officially laid off indefinitely. As we were no longer teaching and planning lessons, we found ourselves with what felt like limitless time. We tried to look at this as a positive: we had more opportunities to see and do things outside of the school. We hadn't intended for our experience to be a vacation per se, but now that we weren't working, we decided to try to embrace it with the time remaining. We were living in George Town, after all. Most days were warm and sunny, and seeing photos of loved ones back home enduring an Edmonton winter always instilled gratitude within me for the privilege I had to be in such a tropical place.

For a little over a week, we ventured outside of George Town to other areas of Penang Island and some larger cities on the mainland. We began to notice the streets looking emptier. People approached each other cautiously, and very few stopped to linger in the streets to talk. Police officers and medical officials began to station themselves in public spaces, entrances to buildings, and upon boarding buses. Our temperature was taken before we were allowed to enter any of these areas.

Our desire to continue the short excursions began to falter as the public atmosphere changed. This wasn't the Malaysia I had come to love. The smells of cuisine no longer permeated the streets. The liveliness and vibrance of the people withdrew. In their absence was eerie quietness and an underlying current of fear in the air that was unsettling. Emma and I began to spend more of our days lounging around the condo, suntanning on the beach, reading, cooking, and chatting. We were in our own private bubble here, able to neglect that things weren't quite right outside of it.

Chapter 7

AFTER HANGING AROUND THE CONDO and realizing we had been back in Malaysia for nearly a month, Emma and I decided to attempt to distance ourselves from the virus's effects. Discussing the best way forward, we decided to reach out to our friend Josh - who had been finishing up his teaching term when we first arrived in George Town. Although we only spent two weeks getting to know him, he had become a good friend. Growing up in a rougher part of London, he was very down to earth. He had an easygoing manner that made us immediately comfortable in his presence. When we last spoke to him, he had planned to travel on to the Philippines. Whether or not he was still there, we didn't know, but we were sure he would have suggestions about what to see, at least.

We heard back from Josh within a few hours. He suggested we meet up with him where he was currently staying in Coron, a beautiful island in the province of Palawan within the Philippines. A small amount of research on the island was all it took to sell us on the idea. It was a diver's paradise, with azure emerald waters, flourishing coral reefs, and World War II shipwrecks begging to be explored. We spent the better part of the afternoon planning snorkelling, kayaking, and hiking excursions. As we made plans, I felt that familiar buzz that comes with knowing a new experience is on the horizon. The excitement was infectious. We set off for Manila - where we would catch a ferry to Coron - the next morning, with the sense of turning over a new leaf.

Although Coron's beauty and boundless opportunity for adventure held enough draw on their own, it appealed to me for a secondary reason. I was eager to be someplace less connected, away from any major cities and towns – someplace the virus didn't seem to be so prevalent. Our trip to Vietnam had been incredible, but the masks and temperature checks were a constant reminder that everything was not as it should be. Being on a small island in the middle of the ocean, I hoped to feel far away from it for a while.

Upon arriving in Manila, we stopped to eat a meal that was a combination of a late lunch and an early dinner before heading to the port. We would then board the overnight ferry to Coron. The last time we ate was before boarding our nine-hour flight and were ravenous. The chicken adobo I ordered from the shopping mall restaurant had never tasted so good. Having refuelled ourselves, we were feeling energized again and chatted excitedly about what we would do in the morning. As we finished up and started to make our way to the port, my phone chimed. Glancing at it quickly, I saw a message from Jai, a friend we had made in one of the hostels we stayed in during our trip to Vietnam. It wasn't until Emma and I were on the ferry that I took the time to read it.

Hey! Just wanted to make sure you and Emma are okay. I booked a flight home. What are you two doing?

Feelings of uneasiness bubbled up inside of me again, numbing the excitement I felt about Coron. "Emma."

"Yeah?"

I looked up from my phone. "I just got a message from Jai. He's leaving Vietnam and going back to Australia."

Emma's forehead creased. "Because of the virus?"

"He didn't say, but I assume so." I held the phone out so she could read it herself. She chewed her lip and pulled her own phone out.

"I got a message from Louisa too. Her and Margaret are also leaving."

Over the next few days, we heard from more friends in Vietnam and Malaysia. Family and friends from home began to contact us as well. My parents were deeply uneasy about us being so far from home. They told us about their own experiences in grocery stores, where panic buying was occurring. Shelves were empty, and they were unable to get even half of what was on their list, including basic necessities like pasta or toilet paper. Although public health officials recommended the use of face masks, disinfectant wipes, and hand sanitizer solutions, there was now a global shortage of these products. There was also some discussion about closing schools. My mother was an elementary teacher and stated that some parents had begun to remove their children from her classroom - just as Aunt Susan's students and parents had done. It was mind-boggling to find out that the virus was now so far-reaching that even Canada was being affected.

I couldn't make up my mind on how I felt about it. On the one hand, it felt so extreme to just leave. We had planned this trip for months, and I was still holding out hope that we'd be able to return to the school to teach. What if we went home, only to realize a few weeks later that we had made a rash judgement? What if going home was essentially giving up? The other voice in my head said it was getting more and more dangerous to stay. I didn't think that Emma and I were likely to die if we contracted the virus. The deaths reported thus far seemed to be attributed to other health conditions that had been worsened by the virus. There was always a chance, though. In addition, this virus was so new, and although some patterns were being observed, it seemed as though no one truly understood yet how it behaved.

We managed to meet up with Josh in Coron and spent an afternoon with him before he moved on to El Nido, another location on Palawan Island. The conversation inevitably returned to the coronavirus topic, and Josh filled us in on his plans.

"I'm staying here, no matter what happens," he said. "Have you heard how many cases there are in London? It's way worse there than it is here. If borders shut and I'm stuck here, I'll be fine. I have contacts I can stay with if things get to that point."

Being stuck in Malaysia or any other country in Asia hadn't occurred to me up until now. While Emma and I had saved up a fair amount of money to fund this trip, it was far from limitless. While my Great Aunt could support us, I didn't want her to have to. The idea that I couldn't go home made me uneasy.

This conversation had made an impact on Emma, too, I found out when we returned to our room that night.

"We can't teach. I don't even think we can travel much anymore, and who knows how long it will be until we can't travel at all. Do you think we should maybe just… go home, too?" She asked, her voice becoming more tentative the longer she spoke. I could tell she didn't want me to agree. I didn't want to, either.

Instead, I said, "I think it's something we should consider."

Solemnly we went to bed with a decision to make burdening our thoughts.

Chapter 8

DECIDING TO GIVE OUR SITUATION some more time to unfold, we thought about what to do with that time.

Josh had suggested two excursions. The first was a guided tour through the sunken Japanese wrecks from World War II, which were filled with multitudes of colorful fish and coral. Here, we snorkelled through the historical and ghostly ruins. Hiking Mount Darala was his second suggestion and we decided to do this on our second day in Coron after Josh left. We hired a cyclo cab (a three-wheeled motorbike) which allowed us to be driven up the scenic, winding dirt road to the start of the hike. The trail wasn't technically a tourist's hike, but rather a service trail that leads to a cell tower; it wasn't manicured for the tourist eye and had random objects scattered about along the way. The hike proved to be challenging, but when we reached the top and towered above the Coron Islands, we were greeted with exquisite views that made every strenuous moment well worth it. As we revelled in the surreal vastness of this quiet trail, our conversation often circled back to the conversation we'd had with Josh. We couldn't shake the worry that we might end up stuck somewhere far away from home.

On our third day in Coron, we decided to head to an area of the wrecks near Lusong Island. It was a spot that was known for phenomenal snorkeling. The water was a sparkling emerald green, and as I looked below the surface into it, I could see a plethora of fish swimming around the old ship beams covered in hard corals. This excursion distracted us from all the negative thoughts surrounding the coronavirus for a few wonderful hours. We swam and laughed and made memories that we'll never forget. A feeling of giddiness came over me, and for the first time in several days, I felt unrestrictedly joyous. When we got back to town, we devoured a local buffet, made conversation with the sociable crowd we immersed ourselves in, and slept well until the early morning light.

We had originally decided to come to Coron in an attempt to escape the threat of the virus in populated cities, despite knowing some of the friends we'd made were starting to go home. However, around the same time we arrived in the beach town, speculation had started that borders all around the world might start to close to limit the spread of the virus. We regularly checked the news and googled flights home while in Coron, though we also tried without success to shake the entrapment of our unease. Although we tried to ignore it, we felt like we no longer belonged here.

By the end of a late breakfast on our fourth day, we had already checked our phones for news updates several times and found ourselves getting antsy. Emma had just asked if we should go to the beach to take our minds off the news for a little while when suddenly both our phone's news alerts started going off.

BREAKING NEWS:

COVID-19 is a rapidly evolving global issue. The Government of Canada will do everything necessary to protect the health, safety, and wellbeing of Canadians, and is working around the clock to limit the spread of this pandemic. This is a critical time, and our top priority remains the safety and security of all Canadians. We request that:

- *All Canadians avoid non-essential travel outside of the country until further notice*
- *Canadian travellers return to Canada via commercial means while they remain available*
- *All travellers to Canada self-isolate for 14 days upon entry, with exceptions for workers who are essential to the movement of goods and people.*

We watched the entire forty-five minute conference to ensure we received all the information, and one fact stood out: we were at least 11 hours away from Manila, the only airport likely to still have flights outbound. It became clear to us both at the same time - it was time to leave. As soon as the live conference ended, we went into problem-solving mode, trying not to panic and make the situation more laborious than it already was. The virus was spreading, faster and faster, and changes were coming by the hour. This was serious, but we still had yet to understand the scope of it.

We started making our way to our room immediately. On our way there, Emma was already reaching out to the friends we had been talking to who hadn't gone home yet, to make sure they had seen the alert and find any more information we didn't have. We received confirmation that the Coron Airport had cancelled nearly all flights, and when we stepped into the hostel, we saw flyers posted across nearly every wall in the building. They stated that all domestic flights within the Philippines would be cancelled within the week, and many international flights would be cancelled next week. We would have to rely on the ferry to get us back to Manila. I called the Manila airport to book our flight home, while Emma tried to book our tickets for the ferry out of Coron to Manila. Nothing about finding our way home would be easy.

Booking the flight proved to be a battle. Every time I connected with someone, I was put on hold, longer and longer each time. I could tell the airline - especially being the only one with outbound international flights nearby - was overwhelmed. When I was finally put through to talk to someone, it was a calm-voiced woman who, despite her efforts to help me, couldn't ease my anxiety when she told me three times in a row, that the flights she was trying to book us for were full or cancelled. Finally, she got us booked for a flight at four o'clock in the morning on March 16th, leaving us with one full day and two nights to get to Manila.

"We'll be home soon," I kept reminding myself. I felt an ounce of relief knowing we had tickets now and wanted to share this with Emma. The feeling was fleeting. As I told her the details, her facial expression fell into concern.

"It's great we have tickets home. But I could only find tickets online for a ferry that leaves tomorrow at six p.m.. We'll have to go down to the terminal to see if there are any earlier departure options." Although she didn't explicitly say so, we were both thinking the same thing: if there were no other options available, we might end up stuck in the Philippines.

We rushed down to the ferry's pier with masks on, trying to look less panicked than we felt. The pace here is quite different from back home. Most people have a slower, more relaxed air about them. The pier wasn't as busy as we had expected, but we could tell things were starting to pick up as people heard the news about the call for international travellers to return home, and about the Coron airport cancelling nearly all of their flights.

As we stood in line for tickets, it steadily grew longer. It seemed that more and more travellers were coming to see what their options were for leaving Coron. We could hear many languages being spoken around us, but the common language was the worry in people's eyes.

We stepped up to the ticket attendant who took our temperatures.

"Hello. Are you an international or local traveller?" He asked in a professional tone.

"International-" We answered simultaneously. I continued, "We're trying to get to Manila airport before our flight at 4 am on March 16th."

"Okay." He seemed ready to hear something like this many times today. "We have one ferry prepared for international travellers returning home. Boarding time is 12:30 p.m. tomorrow, March 15th. Departure is scheduled for 1:15 p.m.. Arrival is at Pier 4 of North Harbour, Manila, near midnight on March 16th. The cost is 2250 pesos per ticket." That would still give us a few hours to get to the airport and through security, if everything went according to plan. It sounded like it was our only option.

"If that's our earliest option..." I trailed off. The attendant nodded. "Then we'll need two tickets, please." We placed our pesos on the desk and he replaced them with our tickets and receipt after asking us about our cabin accommodation preferences.

"We'll see you tomorrow at 12:30 p.m.. Wearing a mask is mandatory, your temperature will be taken upon boarding, and you will be asked to use the hand sanitizing station." We told him we understood and thanked him for his help before turning to head back toward the hostel.

It was only mid-afternoon by the time we got back to our room, but it was near 35°C. Both the heat and the anxiety had tired us out, so we decided to lay down until dinner. I fell asleep thinking about the stunning views I had experienced during the last few days and dreamed about swimming with schools of tropical fish and passing brightly coloured coral reefs, while feeling like a mermaid graciously intertwined with the sea.

EMMA AND I BOTH AWOKE to our room's alarm clock going off at 8:00 a.m..

We crawled out of bed slowly, and I noted how different this morning felt compared to all our others in Southeast Asia; for the first time, I wanted to keep sleeping. After taking a quick shower and packing our belongings, we made our way to the dining area for breakfast, which was provided by the hostel from eight to ten. We made it just in time, and luckily there were still some eggs, toast, and fruit left. We ate mostly in silence, preoccupied with thoughts about the daunting journey ahead of us. Though we had come to Coron in an attempt to escape the virus, it had caught up to us. Abandoning the trip we had planned for months left us feeling defeated and disheartened.

"Do you maybe want to take a walk around before we have to leave? It's only a quarter after ten - we don't have to grab our luggage until twelve-thirty, right?" Emma looked at me with longing in her eyes. I understood that yearning to prolong the experience and take in as much as possible. The last time I had travelled to Malaysia, though I had felt a sadness upon leaving, I had also felt a deep sense of satisfaction. Our premature departure robbed us of that satisfaction and left only sadness behind; my heart went out to her. Though I had done this once before, this was Emma's first trip, and it was coming to an abrupt end that we never could have imagined.

"Sure. A walk is a great idea." I tried to appear as untroubled and excited as possible, though I was really trying not to drown in sorrow over lost adventures. We spent the walk living in the moment as best as we could by avoiding looking at our phones - except to take a few final photos - and breathing in the smell of the salty air.

Time passed all too quickly and by twelve-thirty, we were standing in line to board the ferry to Manila. However, we had failed to remember the frequent delays that come with transit systems in Southeast Asia. Almost every time I had taken a bus or ferry, there had been at least an hour delay. It had never been an annoyance before, and I appreciated that I had become more patient. However, delays were not something we could afford today.

Nonetheless, it was out of our control, and by 1:30 p.m., we were standing in the same place. Emma had moved to one of the plastic chairs lining the waiting room. I was growing impatient and waved Emma over to hold our spot. I walked to the front of the line and asked the attendants what was causing the delay. They informed me that our ferry had a delayed arrival from picking up other passengers from El Nido, another popular tourist spot in Palawan.

Once the ferry finally arrived into the port, we were handed sheets to fill out, asking for details on where we had been in the past two months and about possible symptoms. When we reached the front of the line, we followed the proper procedures and were instructed to hold onto our forms until we arrived in Manila. The ferry was an older model and was already quite crowded.

We walked around the ferry, feeling unprepared to spend the next eleven hours on this boat. As we walked to our cabin, we observed travellers around us. Everyone had the same dynamic of jumpiness, suspicion, and fierce protection of their personal space. Usually, loud chatter and mingling could be heard as people made introductions and shared their travel stories. On this ferry, we heard only low murmurs filled with fears of missing flights home and reflections about how the world had changed.

An hour and a half after we had boarded, a voice came over the intercom system. We expected to hear the Captain reminding us of the safety procedures while on their ferry so that we could depart. Instead, we heard news that caused even more panic and anxiety.

"This is your Captain speaking," he introduced himself in a deep mechanical tone. "We are preparing to depart as soon as we can, but will be behind schedule. There has been a change in plans. We will be docking at Calatagan Port for one hour to pick up the remaining international travellers returning home. We realize that this may be bothersome as everyone is concerned about making their flights. We are doing our best to get everyone to Manila safely and quickly." As confident as he sounded, it was only a mask to hide the concern and responsibility he felt for his passengers.

As soon as he stopped speaking, the low murmur of concerns became more pronounced. Although we, too, had many questions and concerns, Emma and I didn't try to bombard any staff with them. Instead, we curled up to each other and put in our headphones, trying to temporarily ease our minds with music. We knew nothing could be done until we got to Manila. Soon after the Captain's announcement, we felt the ferry undock. Shortly after that, Emma's head drooped heavily on my shoulder, and she succumbed to sleep. I leaned my head gently on hers and let sleep take me too.

I awoke when we heard chatter and shuffling feet outside our cabin door. My head was pounding, and I felt dizzy. Sitting up and stirring a still sleeping Emma, I realized how hungry I was. Gently nudging her awake, she sat up and wiped the sleep from her eyes.

"I think we might be at Calatagan Port. It doesn't feel like we're moving at all. And it sounds like people might be boarding." Nodding, Emma took a deep breath.

"I'm starving. Can we try to track down a meal?" She asked in a slow voice. The bright tone that I was used to hearing in her voice had slowly faded over the last few days and seemed to have vanished completely.

"Yeah, I was thinking the same thing." We found the dining area easily and were surprised to see a considerable number of passengers here as well. The lively late-night atmosphere full of dancing and laughing that I had experienced before on ferries in Asia didn't appear on this voyage. Instead, travellers kept to themselves, rarely interacting with other passengers, ate quickly, and returned to solace in their individual cabins.

We didn't know how long we had already been docked in Calatagan, or how long we would be here. As one of the crew members passed us in the hallway back to our cabin, I decided to ask.

"Excuse me." A young staff member stopped and though he was wearing a mask, the creases around his eyes indicated he was smiling beneath it.

"Yes ma'am, how can I help you?" he asked in a soft tone.

"I'm just wondering how long we've been docked here. We were asleep when we arrived."

He checked his wristwatch and said, "Around one hour. We should be leaving for Manila soon. I don't know the exact departure time."

"Alright, thank you." I tried not to let him see how deep my concern was - it wasn't his problem.

He nodded before continuing in the direction he had been headed. When we arrived back to our room, Emma immediately laid down and covered her face with her pillow.

"Mf hef hrfs." Garbled muffles escaped from under the pillow.

"Emma, are you okay?" I sat down beside her, and felt even more anxiety bubble up inside of me.

She removed the pillow, revealing a pale face underneath. "My head hurts. And I feel so nauseous." The stress of returning home was starting to get to her and we still had multiple flights left to endure.

"Here," I handed her a little pink pill from my bag. "Try taking a Gravol and sleeping for the rest of the trip. It might help." I handed her some water to take the pill with. I knew that motion sickness wasn't the cause of her nausea, but it might help ease the discomfort a little at least.

"Thanks, Colbie." I gave her a supportive smile and let her rest.

My eyes felt heavy, but my mind was racing. What-ifs and thoughts of being stuck in a foreign country far away from home invaded my head. Trying to evade these unpleasant thoughts, I opened up a fantasy novel I had brought with me. I purposefully avoided checking the time to lessen the anxiety I felt about the possibility of missing our flight. It felt like hours before the ferry finally began to move again, and no matter how hard I tried, I could not shake the feeling that we would miss our flight.

By the time the announcement came through the intercom that we were nearly at the port to dock, I had almost accepted the fact that we wouldn't make it. Emma still slept deeply, even snoring quietly. Wanting her to get as much as rest as possible - especially since I hadn't been able to get a wink of sleep over the last few hours - I decided to go for a short walk. In the hallway, people were starting to emerge from their cabins, prepared to leave and rush off to their next destination just as we would. I walked to the main deck and let the seaspray and cool wind wake me up. My eyes fell on the clock, and my heart sank at the sight - five o'clock. We had missed our flight.

Chapter 10

THE LIGHTS ON THE HORIZON shining from Manila would have given me a rush of excitement in any other circumstance. Instead, a chill went down my spine that wasn't from the air. My stomach twisted at the thought of the coming hours. It was time to wake Emma and tell her the news.

After struggling to get to Manila, calming Emma down from a panic attack, and missing our flight by nearly two hours, we arrived at the Ninoy Aquino International Airport. We rushed to the departures level of Terminal 1 and walked up to the line behind the Air Canada check-in desk while struggling to stay far enough away from others and follow all the other safety and prevention procedures.

This airport was packed full of stressed-out people trying to fly home from all over the Philippines. Every step felt chaotic, as though we were in a tornado of uncertainty. This was by far the most hectic place we'd experienced so far. The heavy weight of the dark coronavirus cloud hung above us.

Nearly out of breath, partly from adrenaline and partly from anxiety, we reached the representative, whose name tag said 'Lauren.' She was wearing a mask, but you could tell she had a gentle smile on her mouth underneath it. She took our temperature, as had been done at every encounter with a representative.

"Sanitize your hands," she said, gesturing to the large bottle of sanitizer on the desk. "Tickets please."

We put our tickets on the desk between us and stumbled over our words as we explained the story of how we know we missed the original flight.

"It was because of the Ferry delay-" I started.

"We're Canadians and we just need to get home-" Emma switched off with me.

"And-" My chest was getting tighter as I tried to speak.

"This is a chaotic time for everyone," Lauren interjected gently. "Just try to take a breath while I look for a flight to get you home. What is your final destination?" I appreciated how understanding and patient she was; it helped calm me down too.

"Edmonton, Alberta, Canada," I said, taking the lead in the conversation. I knew that Emma was still shaken from her panic attack and the general stress of the airport environment.

"Okay. Let's see here," Lauren starts. "It looks like there's one last flight I can get you on, but it has a couple layovers." The only flight she could get us on. Wow. We really did almost miss our opportunity to go home.

"That's fine with us," I agreed. What other option did we have?

"Okay. It looks like it is departing in roughly three hours, at 9:45 a.m., with the last boarding call at 9:35 a.m. And oh! It looks like there are two seats together, fortunately. I'll book those for you." Lucky!

"Great. Thank you so much." I said with a smile.

"You're welcome. The first layover will be at the Tokyo airport in Japan. The second will be at the San Francisco airport in California." Upon hearing this information, I felt as though a black hole in my stomach had opened up. The thought of being in any more worldwide hubs made me queasy. Glancing over at Emma, I could tell she was attempting to hide the same feeling of dread.

Trying to stay calm while shrouded in wild thoughts of dubiety, we stayed quiet while Lauren had us place our luggage on the scale one by one before directing us to security and our gate. We said our thank yous and goodbyes to her and walked towards security at a brisk pace. I felt some comfort in the fact that I was not alone in this upside-down trip - that I had my best friend by my side. I reached for Emma's hand as we made our way, holding it tight, and she squeezed tightly in return.

At security, we encountered more of the same. We stayed six feet away from anyone else in the line - as directed, had our temperatures retaken, sanitized our hands for what felt like the hundredth time, and tried not to touch our face or so much as clear our throat in fear of causing anyone around us distress. We answered many questions about where we'd been, the methods of transport we used, and if we had any symptoms of COVID-19, like trouble breathing. The process took almost the entire time we had until boarding closed. As we finally passed through the other side of security, we rushed towards our gate. We hadn't eaten in hours. We were exhausted and more anxious than we'd ever been while travelling. My eyes found every clock as we sped past gate after gate. 9:39. 9:42. 9:44.

At last! A large number 7 came into sight and we barrelled towards it, practically throwing our boarding passes at the gate attendant. It looked like we were the last of the passengers to board this flight. We collapsed into our seats and I felt an immense sense of relief sweep over me as the flight attendants began their announcements.

After four and a half hours, we were soaring over Tokyo, slowly tipping downwards to land. Admiring the surreal view left us speechless. It looked as though the cityscape could go on forever. We came to a rolling stop at the end of the landing strip minutes later, and I felt my anxiety spike again. Although the view overlooking Tokyo had taken my breath away and momentarily distracted me, it then reminded me that we would once again be in a massive world hub stuffed full of desperate travellers. I couldn't wait to be finished with these airports.

"I don't know how well I can handle this. I'm so nervous about continuing to travel through these huge airports with so many people and so much tension." Voicing my own thoughts, Emma spoke in a hushed tone, her eyes glistening with tears. I hugged her tight and brushed her hair softly with my hand.

"I know it's stressful and chaotic and scary, but we can do this. If we could get through Manila, we can get through this, right?" Trying to be as genuine and supportive as I could muster, but I felt my voice waver near the end.

She broke free of my hug and dabbed her tears away with her sleeve before taking a deep, shaky breath and giving me a faltering smile.

"Right. Sorry," she breathed. "Thank you. you've been amazing, Colbie." She tried to continue, but I could see she was holding back more tears.

"It's okay. This has been crazy, but we just need to keep on. We'll be home soon." I smiled supportively and followed her lead, breathing deeply. Nodding, she managed another small smile.

"I can't believe how hungry I am. Hopefully, there's somewhere we can get a quick bite," she said mildly, trying to shift the conversation to a more lighthearted topic as we stood to exit with our backpacks in hand.

"Agreed. Between hunger and exhaustion, I'm feeling pretty weak," I confessed.

There was some nervous chatter about how packed it was going to be as we walked through the twisting hallways towards the arrival hall. Our layover in Tokyo was going to be around six hours. We planned to find food as soon as we passed customs and then try our best to find somewhere that didn't feel overcrowded.

Going through customs didn't take long - we hadn't brought much back since we hadn't shopped much. We ran through the same procedures as we had done at the Manila airport: detailing our travels, taking our temperatures, and completing a questionnaire to ensure we were symptom-free.

Only about half of the passengers on the flight we'd come from - which was already only half capacity - disembarked with us. As we passed through customs, it seemed a little quieter than we had expected. When we stepped off the escalator onto the tiled floor of the departures hall, we stopped dead in our tracks. The hundreds of square feet ahead of us were nearly empty. The breath in my throat caught, and I looked at Emma in shock. It was unsettling to see a space built for thousands of people crammed shoulder-to-shoulder to be borderline empty. The sound of our squeaking shoes and echoing footsteps was a jarring juxtaposition. We hadn't said a word to each other yet; the silence was so eerie that it felt uncomfortable to speak. This was the exact opposite of what we had prepared to step into.

As bizarre as being in a silent airport felt, the relief we felt knowing that we wouldn't have to fight for personal space for the next five hours was immense.

Chapter 11

AFTER THE SIX-HOUR LAYOVER in Tokyo, we boarded the flight to San Francisco. Although this flight was ten hours long, it passed more quickly than expected. I had lost my grasp on time - both in terms of how much had passed, and how much there was to go before we would be in the car heading home. Our last hours in Coron, and even the flight from Manila, felt like they had happened an entire lifetime ago.

Emma and I did not speak much on this flight. We were both trapped in our own minds, too tired to engage with each other and the world around us. Although I was exhausted and often found it challenging to sleep on airplanes, I fell in and out of sleep several times throughout the flight. The quality of this sleep was incredibly subpar. Still, the relentless travel had finally caught up to me, and I was no longer able to remain conscious.

The flight attendants provided us with a meal and snacks throughout the flight. Although the quality of airplane food has improved in recent years, I found it difficult to eat, despite knowing I needed to sustain my energy. The stiffness pervading my muscles and the foggy haze that seemed to cloud my mind made my stomach churn. I forced myself to swallow a few bites, but it left me unsatisfied and craving the fresh, fragrant food I had become accustomed to consuming in Malaysia.

As we began our descent into San Francisco, the sunrise spilt into the small windows. That reassuring bump of the airplane wheels against the runway jolted me into feeling a little more alert and inspired a new sense of calm in me. Knowing I was about to get off this plane and walk around a wide, open space brightened my outlook.

After emerging from customs and confirming again that we weren't experiencing any symptoms of COVID-19, we made a beeline for the washroom. Here, we took some time to change into a fresh pair of clothing from our carry-ons, wash our faces, brush our teeth, and apply deodorant. While all I really wanted to do was take a long, hot shower, just being able to freshen up felt refreshing. I almost felt human again.

For the last time, Emma and I went through security and arrived in the international departures hall, where we would wait for our final flight to Edmonton. To compensate for the airplane food, we decided to treat ourselves to a restaurant meal. Most of the food locations were closed, but there was a grill with American-style options still open where we ordered hamburgers and fries. Having fresh, hot, restaurant-style comfort food did a lot to boost our morale. Emma even became chattier and brighter than she had been in the last couple of days.

Being more alert and having a considerable amount of time to kill before we had to board our flight, I pulled out my phone and connected to the complimentary airport Wi-Fi. I took some time to catch up on the developing situation. At this point in the pandemic, things were changing almost hourly.

Since March 14th, when Justin Trudeau had called for all Canadians abroad to return home, a few coronavirus vaccine trials had been scheduled to start. While this seemed promising, I knew that clinical trials were a lengthy process. It often took close to, or over a year until treatment was ready to be approved for public sale. Still, it was comforting to see that efforts were being made to control this virus in a more permanent way. If a vaccine was developed, I might be able to return to Malaysia sooner than later.

After browsing news articles, it quickly became apparent that countries across the world were dealing with coronavirus in very different ways. The differential treatment towards the virus seemed to be based on differing understandings of how dangerous COVID-19 actually was. This uncertainty, not just on the individual level but also politically, was one of the main reasons that Emma and I had deferred coming home for so long. A pandemic on this scale was so different from anything the world had seen before - past experiences and policies couldn't be relied upon. I had a feeling that the effectiveness of governmental responses to the virus could only be known retrospectively.

In Italy, thousands had tested positive, and many were dying. Italian officials urged other countries to take the pandemic seriously and take immediate action to prevent its spread. In the United States, President Donald Trump was criticized for maintaining a stance that the situation was being blown out of proportion. Although it seemed that he was eventually changing his tune, he was now seeking to obtain exclusive rights to a vaccine being developed in Germany. In the United Kingdom, the government proposed a "herd immunity" strategy to deal with the pandemic. This strategy seemed to involve encouraging only the most vulnerable stay home while the rest of the population carried on, as usual, hoping that they would become ill and recover, thereby becoming immune and reducing the transmission of the virus down the road.

Public reaction in the U.K. expressed profound anxiety over a lack of instruction from their government. I was reassured to see that the Canadian government was taking decisive action to implement preventative measures, rather than just playing it day-by-day and hoping for the best. Many customer-facing businesses were closing indefinitely, including gyms, health centres, bars, restaurants, movie theatres, shopping centres, banks, and tourist attractions. Industries with non-essential workers were asking their employees to work from home. A mutual ban on all but essential travel across Canada and the United States border was in the works. Many professional sports leagues were also suspending games, and provincial and municipal elections were being postponed.

The situation was developing vigorously across Canada. British Columbia reported three new coronavirus deaths. Ontario's first death was just recorded, along with a confirmed 32 new cases, bringing the total number of cases in that province to 177. British Columbia had decided to close all their public schools indefinitely, while Ontario extended spring breaks. Cases were rising in Alberta as well. The Premier of Alberta, Jason Kenney, had declared a public health emergency that morning.

The more I read, the more it seemed clear to me that this was just the beginning. I still felt a crushing sensation in my chest, mourning the experiences Emma and I had lost out on. However, I now felt equally confident in our decision to return to Canada.

Chapter 12

"NOW BOARDING PASSENGERS for Flight 229 to Edmonton." A booming voice overhead announces.

I breathed a sigh of relief at the same time a wave of revulsion washed over me at the thought of stepping onto yet another airplane. "Just one last flight," I reminded myself, "and we'll finally be home."

Although we were boarding an international flight, the passengers were entirely Canadian nationals. Most seemed to be under the age of thirty. The border had closed to all international travellers, and only those with Canadian passports were allowed to board the airplane. We were lucky enough to get seats at the front of the plane, so we were among the last to board.

The plane was at least half empty, as the others had been. Most people were already pulling out their hand sanitizers and disinfectant wipes to clean the armrests and headrests of their seats. Some wore face masks. While I was used to seeing face coverings in Asia, seeing it on a plane full of Canadian nationals was jarring and reminded me just how up-side-down the world was right now. Light chatter ensued throughout the cabin, and I found the Canadian tones comforting. Despite my utter exhaustion, my mind felt unexpectedly sharp.

"I never want to get on another plane, ever, after this," Emma groaned as we organized our space.

"Me neither," I agreed, though I knew we'd both feel differently in a few days. "This has been the longest few days of my life."

"Few days? Where did you come from?" A man around our age spoke up from across the aisle. He introduced himself as James, and we learned that he had spent the last couple of months volunteering in Mexico. Emma and I took turns recounting the previous few days. As we talked, a few other passengers listened in and joined the conversation by narrating their experiences. Most had booked flights following Trudeau's announcement, the same as we had done.

Elizabeth had been living in England on a work visa that was due to expire in December of this year. It was a one-time visa, so the opportunity to work there wouldn't come up readily for her again.

"The United Kingdom feels like home to me - more than Canada ever has - so I wanted to try to start a life there. I have a lot of experience in tourism, so the plan was to work in a hotel or something. I had an interview for a position in a historic hotel in Exeter - this awesome medieval town in the southwest of England. I was going to start my master's degree in England in September. But the virus is really spreading there, and hotels are shutting down. Tourism is pretty much dead, and I was running out of money. I was worried I'd be stranded in the U.K. without a job, so I decided to come home." She told us.

"Will you go back for school?" Emma asked.

She pursed her lips. "I'm really not sure. I thought I'd have more money saved up for tuition at this point, but I don't know what kind of job I'll be able to find right now in Canada, either." My mind wandered as I thought about my own job prospects. I had saved up a lot of money for Malaysia, but the cost of living in Canada was much higher. And the thought of being stuck with nothing to do for weeks on end wasn't an appealing one. At least I was lucky enough to be staying with my parents during my isolation period. That should give me some time to figure things out better.

A girl named Samantha spoke up. "I know what you mean about going to school. I was just finishing my first year of medical school in Switzerland. Exams are starting in a few weeks; I should be studying right now."

"Are your exams cancelled then?" I asked.

"I wish! I'll have to take them online from home, even though some are going to be at like three in the morning with the time difference. I just didn't want to risk staying and getting stuck. Like Elizabeth, I need to work to pay for my rent over the summer. At least in Edmonton, I'll be able to stay with my parents rent-free. I'm not sure if it was the right choice, though."

I thought about friends back home who were finishing their degrees this year. Would they be able to graduate? Attend convocation? I felt overwhelmingly grateful that I had graduated the year before and had been able to celebrate that significant milestone in my life with all of my friends and family. To have those four years of dedication and sleepless nights end so underwhelmingly would be remarkably disappointing.

"Yeah, I mean… it's kind of a worldwide thing, isn't it?" James interjected. "Some countries have it worse, of course. I have a friend in Italy, and it's just scary there. So many people have died already. But regardless of where you go, things are shutting down. I don't know if Canada will be any different."

There was a pause. It was tough to wrap my head around just how dramatically this thing had shaken up peoples' lives. It had utterly disrupted every possible kind of plan and seemed to have put a firm standstill on time. For it to have touched so many people across virtually every country, for this experience to be quite literally universal… I hadn't lived through an event this far-reaching in my lifetime. It felt monumental.

The girl from Switzerland spoke up. "I'd say by June or July, things will be back to normal.. Right?"

"Yeah," I agreed, brightening a bit at the thought. "We just have to sit tight for a bit. This is just temporary." Temporary as I thought it would be, I couldn't bring myself to imagine what my life would look like after the two weeks of mandatory quarantine. The plan had always been to finish my degree and travel. I didn't have a plan B. Although I was truly exhausted, more so than I had ever been, it felt like the real challenge was yet to come.

Chapter 13

AFTER TWO VERY LONG, exhausting days of travel, we finally landed safely back in Edmonton. I passed through the arrivals terminal door to find my Dad waiting for me. But a space that used to be full of excitement, heartfelt welcomes, and spirited story-telling, now felt like a place I no longer wanted to linger longer than necessary. So with a quick hug and an offering to carry my bag, we were out.

We walked Emma to where her sister was waiting to pick her up just outside the terminal doors. After she lifted her backpack into the trunk of the car she turned to give me a hug goodbye.

"I'll see you in a couple of weeks, okay?" I said over Emma's shoulder in a tight embrace.

"See you in a couple of weeks," Emma echoed back to me.

With so much still to be understood about how this virus operated, spread, and how its symptoms manifested in different individuals, the only chance to prevent its spread was to avoid contact with others. Because of this, my Dad didn't allow us to make any stops once we were in the car. It was a three-hour-long drive to my parent's house, where I would be staying. I headed into a mandatory two-week self-isolation, which meant I was to stay indoors: no one was allowed to come in or out. There would be no visitors, no trips to the grocery store, no physical contact with the outside world around me - for any reason. I was being quarantined.

Although my parent's home was not at all where I had expected to be in what was supposed to be the middle of my travels, there was a comfort in being here. I was safe, and I managed to keep myself busy indoors. At least during the first couple of days.

I tried my hand at breadmaking - a popular activity for many in my generation during isolation, from what I saw online. I found ways to stay active inside the house and tried to get creative to pass the time. Most importantly, I was doing my part to help stop the spread of this novel coronavirus. I showed no symptoms, and I was optimistic that after these two weeks, I would be able to embrace my friends and tell them face-to-face about my roller coaster adventure.

However, with every daily news update from the Chief Medical Officer, my expectations about what my life would look like after this quarantine period quickly changed. Canada was effectively trying to flatten the curve: meaning health and government officials were trying to slow the spread of the virus to reduce the number of people seeking treatment. This would, in turn, prevent overwhelming our medical system, a grave situation that was being faced by other countries around the world. Therefore, businesses deemed non-essential were forced to temporarily close their doors, including restaurants, hair salons, clothing stores and even dentist offices. Companies that could conduct the same work out of office were sending their employees to work from home. The others that couldn't were forced to lay off their employees. Everyone was asked to self-isolate and socially distance from anyone not living in the same household as them, regardless of whether or not they had travelled internationally. Gatherings were restricted to no more than 10 people indoors and only in spaces that could accommodate two meters between all individuals at all times. Canadians were asked not to hug, shake hands, or interact unnecessarily with one another.

I wanted to stay informed about the pandemic but felt overwhelmed with daily updates - an unnerving mix. As part of Canada's Economic Response Plan, they provided a Canadian Emergency Response Benefit (CERB) to citizens financially affected by COVID-19. Those eligible would receive $500 per week, for up to sixteen weeks. News reports were peppered with phrases like "expect cautionary measures to be in place until at least..." followed by a vague range of dates stretching months into the future. It became increasingly difficult to wrap my head around just how long this would last and what life would look like in the meantime.

As isolation dragged on, I found myself thinking more about Aunt Susan, George Town, and Wendy. I had been in contact with my aunt upon arriving home. Our departure had been so abrupt that we left several of our belongings at her condo, expecting to return there after Coron. She assured us she would keep our things there until the next time we were in Malaysia. The idea that I would be there again seemed impossible.

I regularly checked the news in Malaysia, often worried about the people I had come to know and love. There were usually about 100 to 200 new cases of COVID-19 reported each day, but most were in Kuala Lumpur. To date, Penang has only had a little over 100 confirmed cases, and only one death. I wondered if I would have been safer waiting out the pandemic in George Town. My mind went in circles as I analyzed the events and decisions that led Emma and I back to Edmonton. It was impossible to know if we had made the right choices. Being with my parents during such an uncertain time reassured me that we did, though.

Chapter 14

WHEN I LEFT THE EDMONTON AIRPORT that day back in March, I didn't realize it would be the last time I was in a public space for months. It was now the middle of May, and I was still isolating at my parents' home. It wasn't just me - many people around the country had been quarantined from friends and family for months. Because of the restrictions on group gatherings, people started to postpone weddings, rethink graduation celebrations, and find creative ways to celebrate monumental moments in life without gathering.

I hadn't yet visited any of my friends, but we found other fun ways to keep in contact, often with group video calls. I found myself measuring the length of isolation in the length of my friends' growing locks. Seeing my friends grow shaggier with every call added humour to a disheartening situation. It was a reminder we were living in a time much different from the one we had been in before: one without the amenities we were accustomed to, like regular haircuts, shopping trips, and religious ceremonies.

Some days it felt nearly impossible to get any footing under me for moving into the immediate future, let alone the distant future. I had no way to grasp exactly what that would look like. There were no reliable answers about when - or even if - this would all be over, or when life would start to resemble what it was before COVID-19 began altering it. Today was just one of those days. I decided to video call Emma, her unwavering positivity always grounded me.

Emma's face popped up on my laptop screen as the video connected. "Emma! Hi, how are you?"

"Hi! I'm good. A little bored around here today, but good! How are you? How's the job hunt going?"

"Honestly? Not so great. There just aren't many people hiring right now, and with so many people in similar positions trying to find work, it's been really tough."

Although I found myself explaining this to Emma, I knew she was on the exact same page. Both of us had been trying to find work since our mandatory isolation had finished, and it was proving to be no easy task. I didn't anticipate that the next time I searched for work would be in the middle of a pandemic. I had expected that once I returned home from Asia, finding a new job might take a bit of time, but not nearly as long as it was now.

I also thought that having a newly attained university degree would work in my favour. Unfortunately, this was no longer the case. With so many people out of work, everyone was competing for the same jobs. It didn't matter if they were skilled labourers, highly educated professionals, or retail workers. No industry hadn't been affected in some way by this virus.

"I'm in the same boat," Emma replied, "I was messaging with Louisa a couple days ago, and she's experiencing the same thing over in Sweden. She told me that Margaret returned to work at a bakery she had been at before they left to teach at myTESOL. It was deemed essential, and she's been swamped in all this. Louisa hasn't been as lucky thus far with finding work."

Emma and I had also been group messaging with Josh since we had gone home. He had decided to stay in Malaysia and recently told us that he was having trouble finding a job.

"At least we're all in this together," I said to Emma, "I could've never imagined an event that plagues all four corners of the map."

It was slightly comforting to know I wasn't alone struggling for unemployment. At the same time, knowing that so many were also failing to find work, and would continue to do so for the foreseeable future, was unnerving. Many of my friends finishing their last semester of school had hoped to find summer jobs but out of luck. Like me, they didn't qualify for the Canada Emergency Response Benefit (CERB). Though it was a help for qualified people, many fell through the gaps due to certain restrictions. Those who were unemployed in Canada before COVID-19 did not qualify, nor did students who relied on full-time summer employment to pay for the following fall semester tuition. There was no monetary help for them.

At the same time, having finished up their semester's coursework and examinations online, post-secondary students were notified that they wouldn't be returning to campus in the fall either. Classes would continue to be held online for at least another semester to ensure staff and students' safety. While the schools couldn't be blamed for putting safety first, many were weighing the pros and cons of whether online classes could replace the value of face-to-face learning.

I felt a heaviness in my chest, thinking about the people greatly affected by this pandemic - not just a result of the economic and social disruption, also those whose loved ones were high risk, tested positive for COVID-19, and especially those who lost their battle against it. I had to remind myself that, though this experience had taken a toll on my mental health, I was so lucky to be in a safe and secure home.

TI remained grateful for my fortunate living situation and the fantastic support network I had. Yet, part of me yearned for the days when all I had to worry about was deciding what I would teach during my next lesson and where I would travel during the next break between schooldays. I couldn't believe that had just been a few short months ago; it felt like a lifetime had passed. I didn't know what course this pandemic would take or how it would be written in the history books. What I did know was that it would be a long time before I would be able to enjoy an unadulterated passion for travel again. And although there were greater obstacles to face, for this brief moment, I allowed myself to mourn the life I had before this all began.

Afterword

AT THE TIME OF WRITING, COVID-19 is still extremely prevalent across the globe. Though different countries have established their own sets of preventative measures, some areas have been hit harder than others. It remains a global issue and the most difficult challenge the world has had to face since the Second World War[5]. Because of this, recreational international travel remains a pipe dream, and it is nearly impossible to predict when this new reality will abate. That being said, as countries and cities around the world determine the best ways to reopen to the public, travel and tourism are sure to be at least partially included in this process.

Although the idea of a vacation is currently far from the minds of many, travel restrictions have been lifted in a significant number of countries. The European Union and the United Kingdom have opened borders to many countries, including Canada. A number of Caribbean countries including Barbados, Jamaica, and St. Lucia have opened for tourists from numerous countries to visit, as long as they are willing to comply with new measures put in place to prevent the spread[6]. For example, those who wish to travel to Barbados from higher risk countries must take a COVID-19 test at least 72 hours before departing, while those from lower risk countries must be tested at least one week beforehand. Visitors must also complete an online Embarkation/Disembarkation Card that lists a series of questions related to COVID-19 symptoms[7]. Other countries opening the door to tourism have put similar requirements in place. However, many governments are still advising against nonessential international travel.

---

5   United Nations, 2020.
6   CNN, 2020.
7   CNN, 2020.

To date, Canada has only allowed Canadian nationals and permanent residents, and their immediate family members to enter the country in an attempt to prevent nonessential travel. Those entering the country must quarantine for 14 days upon arrival[8]. There are some travelers from the United States exempt from this travel ban, including temporary foreign workers, some international students, those approved for permanent residency but are not yet permanent residents, accredited diplomats and their immediate family members, and airforce and marine crew members[9].

The economy has taken a hit on a global scale, but some countries face additional challenges getting their feet back on the ground - especially those reliant on tourism. Some countries have emphasized the establishment of safe ways to welcome back travelers. Mexico's "Come to Cancun 2x1" campaign offers two free nights accommodation for every two nights paid and will reimburse one of two plane tickets. Numerous hotels in Thailand offer "buy one get one free" promotions for accommodation, and Uzbekistan offers $3,000 in compensation for tourists who contract COVID-19 while there[10]. Though many countries have begun to attempt adaptations to accommodate a new era of travel, safety still takes precedence over a good deal for many reluctant to travel until a vaccine is introduced and made accessible.

Looking forward to the possibility of a post-pandemic world, it is difficult to determine specifically how international travel will be affected in the long term, and what measures might permanently be put in place in airports and other centers popular for travelers. We can be quite certain that there will be changes made to the traveling experience, and those hoping to travel internationally will have to learn to adapt to new ways of doing so. It is likely that there will be some forms of "interlocking safe zones"[11] in future travel, resulting in some countries being permitted to cross a given border while others are not. Industries related to tourism are likely to raise prices and put in safety measures to prevent overtourism. Fewer will be able to travel due to increased cost, especially

---

8   Government of Canada, 2020b.
9   Government of Canada, 2020b.
10   CNN, 2020.
11   Foreign Policy, 2020.

considering personal financial burdens caused by the pandemic. Taking fewer trips and remaining at a vacation destination for longer periods of time are expected to become a modern, ethical, and sustainable form of travel, but this is also not easy for those working or on a budget.

It is entirely possible that the cruise industry will be changed forever, as the elderly - a large demographic of cruise ship passengers - are less likely to travel. After cases of COVID-19 affected cruises like the Artania, on which 36 passengers were tested positive for the virus in March[12], many have felt the urge to avoid high risk situations such as this, putting the industry at a halt for the time being. It is also predicted that poorer, developing countries will be the last to recover[13], and biosafety procedures such as temperature checks and masks are here for the foreseeable future. To ensure proper social distancing guidelines are followed, many tourist attractions must lower maximum capacities. Booked time slots for popular tourist attractions like museums and galleries are likely to become more common. An example of this is the Louvre in Paris - to ensure maximum safety, all visitors are required to book a time slot, follow social distancing measures, and wear a mask at the museum.

There will remain, of course, the ethical dilemma of tourism during the pandemic. Though many preventative measures have been put in place across the world, prevention still comes down to individual action and the individual's responsibility to avoid spreading the virus, especially in areas with limited access to medical systems that cannot support an outbreak at high capacity. Unfortunately, a fair portion of these countries are also those reliant on tourism for their economy. Air travel itself poses a greater risk of spreading the virus, even when social distancing measures are complied with. Airlines have a break-even load factor of 75 - 80%, so capping capacity at 50 to 60% for social distancing is not sustainable, making distancing on planes unattainable for the future without increasing prices. Masks while flying, social distancing measures, and contactless technology are expected to become the standard in airports, even when international travel becomes more regular[14]. It will be a balancing act between keeping travel and tourism a possibility

---

12   CTV, 2020.
13   Foreign Policy, 2020.
14   Washington Post, 2020.

and preventing the spread of the virus, but it is likely that travel will still be possible, as it is valued globally.

The hindrances put in place for those pursuing international travel may persuade many to turn their focus towards domestic travel. For Canadians, this is especially true during the warmer months. Travelers within Canada may be subject to provincial or territorial border restrictions. Those arriving in the Northwest Territories must mandatorily self-isolate for 14 days in Yellowknife, Inuvik, Hay River, or Fort Smith only[15]. This measure is essential for protecting Indigenous communities in Canada, which are more vulnerable to COVID-19. However, for the most part, domestic travel is still possible, especially within one's own province. A positive side of this is that Canadians have the opportunity to discover lesser known Canadian destinations and attractions. A greater familiarity with Canadian towns and smaller cities combined with the popularity of travel blogs and Instagram travel accounts has the potential to shed light on places the rest of the world has never heard of and could consider visiting once travel restrictions to Canada have been lifted. Travel will remain possible, even for those with a greater financial burden, if one knows where to go.

---

15 Government of Northwest Territories, 2020.

Bibliography

CNN. (2020). Which international destinations are reopening to tourists? Retrieved August 9, 2020, from https://www.cnn.com/travel/article/global-destinations-reopening-to-tourists

CNN. (2020). From free flights to COVID-19 payouts: Can travel incentives lure visitors back? Retrieved August 9, 2020, from https://www.cnn.com/travel/article/can-travel-incentives-lure-visitors-back/index.html

CTV. (2020). After months at sea, the final cruise ship carrying passengers makes it home. Retrieved August 9, 2020, from https://www.ctvnews.ca/world/after-months-at-sea-the-final-cruise-ship-carrying-passengers-makes-it-home

Foreign Policy. (2020). The Future of Travel After the Coronavirus Pandemic. Retrieved August 9, 2020, from https://foreignpolicy.com/2020/06/13/travel-tourism-coronavirus-pandemic-future/

Globe and Mail. (2020). Canadians abroad urged to come home amid tightening travel restrictions due to Coronavirus. Retrieved July 11, 2020, from https://www.theglobeandmail.com/canada/article-canadians-abroad-urged-to-come-home-while-they-still-can-amid/

Government of Canada. (2020a). Coronavirus disease (COVID-19): Symptoms and treatment. Retrieved June 9, 2020, from https://www.canada.ca/en/public-health/services/diseases/2019-novel-coronavirus-infection/symptoms.html?topic=ex-col-faq#a

Government of Canada. (2020b). Coronavirus disease (COVID-19): Who can travel to Canada - citizens, permanent residents, foreign nationals and refugees. Retrieved August 9, 2020, from https://www.canada.ca/en/immigration-refugees-citizenship/services/coronavirus-covid19/travel-restrictions-exemptions.html

Government of Northwest Territories. (2020). Travellers arriving in the NWT. Retrieved August 9, 2020, from https://www.gov.nt.ca/covid-19/en/services/travel-moving-around/travellers-arriving-nwt

Kantis, C., Kiernan, S., & Bardi, J.S. (2020). Updated: Timeline of the coronavirus. Think Global Health. Retrieved June 9, 2020, from https://www.thinkglobalhealth.org/article/updated-timeline-coronavirus

United Nations. (2020). COVID-19 Response. Retrieved August 9, 2020, from https://www.un.org/en/coronavirus/un-secretary-general

Washington Post. (2020). 11 ways the pandemic will change travel. Retrieved August 7, 2020, from https://www.washingtonpost.com/travel/2020/06/15/11-ways-pandemic-will-change-travel/

World Health Organization. (2018). Managing epidemics: key facts about major deadly diseases. Geneva.